ONCE UPON A DREAM

South East Verses

Edited By Donna Samworth

First published in Great Britain in 2017 by:

Young Writers
Remus House
Coltsfoot Drive
Peterborough
PE2 9BF
Telephone: 01733 890066
Website: www.youngwriters.co.uk

FOREWORD

Welcome Readers!

Dreams play a big role in our life, whether from the worlds that keep us entertained at night to the dreams and ambitions we aspire to in the future, so it was only fitting we used this as our topic for our latest nationwide primary school competition.

I am proud to present 'Once Upon A Dream – South East Verses', a collection of poetic treasures that will make your imaginations run wild. Among these pages you will find a variety of poetic styles, from dream acrostics to candy land couplets to fear provoking free verse. Some poems may leave you jumping for joy, some may tickle your sides, while others may pull at your heart strings as each author becomes their own dream catcher.

The selection process, while difficult, proved to be a very rewarding task and I hope you enjoy the range of work that has made it to the final stages. With so many wonderful poems featured in this anthology picking a winner was another very difficult task so well done to *Samuel Rummery* who has been chosen as the best poet. I'd also like to congratulate all the young writers featured in this collection.

Finally, I hope you find the poems that lie within these pages just as entertaining as I did and I hope it is kept as a keepsake for many years to come.

Donna Samworth

CONTENTS

St Andrew's CE Primary School, Nuthurst

Joe Finan (9)	58

St Michael's Junior School, Galleywood

Daniel Selden (9)	59
Abbie Rogers (10)	60
Rhianna Dunkley (10)	62
Harry Jacobs (10)	64
Christopher Daly (10)	66
Lucas Marsh (10)	67
Evan Flack (11)	68
Olivia Davanzo (11)	69
Hannah Samuels (10)	70
Bobbi Lyla Brook (11)	71
Alfie Palmer (10)	72
Joely Lovett (10)	73
Alexandra Bacon (9)	74
Leon Kuhanuka (9)	76
Alfie James England (10)	77
Jessica Merrifield (8)	78
Ethan Samuels (9)	79
Hope Abigail Burchell (11)	80
Louis Roberts (8)	81
Shweta Sharma (10)	82
Chloe Rose Taylor (11)	83
Layla Grace McClean (10)	84
Daniel Hudson (10)	85
Lewis Powell (9)	86
Oscar Harverson (11)	87
James White (9)	88
Ruth Selden (11)	89
Joseph Nicholls (10)	90
Noah Amir Taylor (10)	91
Ruby Carroll (8)	92
Harry Brown (9)	93
Beth Kirk (10)	94
Lola Flack (8)	95
Emily Kerwin (10)	96
Raffael Ollivier (8)	97
Ashton Scott (10)	98
Charlie John Davis (10)	99
Jack Devey (9)	100
Patrick Barrow (11)	101
Ethan Edwards (11)	102
Rudy Don Golding (10)	103
Hollie Brook (9)	104
Issy Caviel (8)	105
Tom Beales (10)	106
Isla Gurden (11)	107
Jonathan Wakeling (10)	108
Emma Cox (9)	109
Daniel Gardner (10)	110
Sophie Shead (9)	111
Alasdair John Gray (9)	112
Rhianna Riley (9)	113
Chloe Southgate (8)	114
Jessica Barrow (9)	115
Millie Melvin (11)	116
Rebecca Samuels (10)	117
Chloe Bull (11)	118
Mia Coetser (8)	119
Katie Walpole-Bennett (10)	120
Lauri Roberts (9)	121
Esme Alty (9)	122
Chloe Williams (10)	123
Harrison Whiteside (7)	124
Evelyn Tumbridge (8)	125
Niamh Keenan (9)	126
Keziah Joy Burchell (9)	127
Weronika Piotrowska (8)	128
Imogen Ayres (8)	129
Shay Turner (9)	130
Andrew Frain (10)	131
Olly Sweeting (8)	132
Oren Lindo (9)	133
Lucian Richardson (7)	134
Ruhayla Abdullah (8)	135
Alex Foulston (8)	136
Konrad Philpott (10)	137
Max Baulch (8)	138
Jasmine Ellouise Potter (8)	139
Oliver Lakin (9)	140
Katie Cox (7)	141

St Peter's Primary School, South Croydon

Mayeisha Pelis (9)	142
Lola Manvatkar (8)	143
Reece Bailey (8)	144
Lily Steele (8)	145
Raluca Maria Tataru (9)	146
Victoria Pliszka (8)	147
Alice Peterson (8)	148
Jacob Fitzgerald (9)	149
Sarmad Ahmad (8)	150
Isaac Kirkwood-Ayres (8)	151

Vinehall School, Mountfield

Freddie Lawler (10)	152
Annabel Aoife Quill (10)	154
Dexter Bell (10)	156
Billy Mannion (10)	157
Tilly Richardson (9)	158
Connie Soan (10)	159
Gabriella America Brewer (10)	160
Edith Daphne Forder (9)	161
Isak Syltevik Dobson (10)	162

THE POEMS

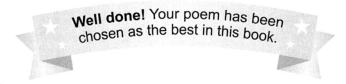

Well done! Your poem has been chosen as the best in this book.

Running With The Wolves

I'm running with the wolves
I'm running with the pack
I'm running with the wolves
There is no looking back.

I'm running with the wolves
I'm running in the snow
I'm running with the wolves
And it's zero and below.

I'm running with the wolves
We're going for the kill
I'm running with the wolves
It gives me such a thrill.

I'm running with the wolves
I'm playing with the young
I'm running with the wolves
I'm having so much fun.

I'm running with the wolves
The snow has turned to clover
I'm running with the wolves
My dream is almost over.

Samuel Rummery (10)
Vinehall School, Mountfield

Killer Clowns

Twisted faces obscured my view,
Fear gripped my body, through and through,
My heart thumped loudly and leapt with fear,
Voices were taunting me, I could not hear.

A stab of pain sent me falling to the floor,
I was in so much agony, I could take no more,
The sound of chainsaws drowned out my plea,
I begged for mercy, I wanted to be free.

The clowns laughed loudly with venom in their eyes,
They told me to surrender and say my goodbyes.
I clenched my fists, I had to fight,
I refused to be their victim, in the dead of night.

So with fire in my soul and fury in my eyes,
I lashed out blindly and forced myself to rise.
I fought them bravely, one by one,
The clowns were dead, the deed was done.

I stirred in my bed as the sun peeked through,
It was a beautiful morning, bright and blue.
The night was over, I was safe and well,
I had escaped from the clowns in my nightmare of hell.

Alayna Ahmed (11)
Fairlop Primary School, Hainault

At War With Peace

M y friends and I, walking together
A dmiring what we see
G lowing flowers blooming bright and beautiful
I ndigo butterflies fluttering around
C runchy leaves, just begging to be eaten
A ll have one thing in common
L iving their lives together

P eople sounding the sirens
L aughing is for later
A s we are at war
C alling people to safety
E veryone screams and runs
S cary black bombs disrupt the silence of waiting

D ipping in and out of the river
O penly showing their happiness to us
N umerous species of fish living in harmony
T his is what we want for the world

D ropping the bombs on innocent people's homes
O nly could mean one thing: we fight back

W hereas, on this trip, my friends have spotted no
   harm
A nd neither have I
R eally, we are all just fighting ourselves and that isn't
   right.

Hasna Khan (10)
Fairlop Primary School, Hainault

My Family

I love my family,
they never give me a fright.
We live so happily,
they always kiss me goodnight.

My dad is so precious,
I always get what I want,
he never gets suspicious
but always makes his pen blunt.

My beautiful mum's next,
what would I do without Mum?
She's the absolute best,
but she will never drink rum!

My bro is the eldest,
he loves things that he can wreck,
when out, he's the shyest,
his talent is using tech.

Syeda is her name
her speciality's art.
She loves a candy cane,
and she has a big heart!

There is my family,
I love them very dearly,
and they love some Bramley,
now you all know me clearly!

Nawsin Sharmila (10)
Fairlop Primary School, Hainault

Lost

I hold my mother's hand tightly
Scared and afraid to let go,
It's OK she says, kissing my forehead lightly
Guiding me through the snow.

I walked into the sweet shop
Finding sugary delights everywhere,
Happily, I look behind and stop
My mother was definitely not there.

The world implodes on itself
And grotesque puppets loom over me,
For in this world I am just an elf
Without my loving parents, a refugee.

Bullets of rain quickly lashing down
Dampening my skirt,
Now I suppress my tears and frown
The street is like a desert.

All of a sudden I am awake
In my mother's arms,
Just relieved it was a dream
And away from harm.

Zara Nithin (11)
Fairlop Primary School, Hainault

The Secret Door...

A magical door is what I see,
Is this door just for me?
Is this really what I see?
This doesn't make any sense to me.

I go ahead and open the magical door,
I see a glistening marble floor.
I dance to my heart's content,
As I dance, I breathe a beautiful floral scent.

My hair blows in the gentle wind,
I don't stop singing and dancing.
I am surrounded by a forest of candy trees,
Sweets and chocolates is what I can see.

I wonder what my mum would say,
If I eat all this candy and chocolate today.
Here I am on my own, having so much fun alone,
For everything I have seen...
I will never ever forget this dream.

Fariha Azam (10)
Fairlop Primary School, Hainault

We Are The Pirates

We are the pirates, we are the pirates
Of the seven seas, of the seven seas.
We are the pirates, we are the pirates
Take a look at me!

We're sailing on the sea, it's dark and eerie
We won't surrender, even if you plea.

We are the pirates, we are the pirates
Of the seven seas, of the seven seas.
We are the pirates, we are the pirates
Take a look at me!

We're on the island looking for money
The people here don't find it funny.
We won't surrender,
Even if you plea!

Emily Ward (10)
Fairlop Primary School, Hainault

Inside The Magic Door I Saw...

Inside the magic door I saw:
A beautiful garden and a sycamore,
Roses growing here and there,
An enchanted substance that wards off bears,
As well as this I met loads of animals
Even a couple of penguins doing cannonballs!

Some amazing things I did not see:
The busy hive of a bumblebee,
The buzzing was ever so clear to me,
Splashes of water dripping from my hair,
I possibly past a lion in its lair,
This incredible place - what does this mean?

Oh no! I've woken up! It was just a dream!

Jennifer Balaji (11)
Fairlop Primary School, Hainault

100 Years In The Future

There was an open archway
With silvery-grey and dark blue misty spirals
Swirling inside the door.

'100 years in the future'
It said on the floor
It was a portal
Heaven knows to where
Carelessly, I stepped inside
And landed somewhere
As I opened my eyes
I saw I was in a street.
But the sight I could see
Was not all nice and sweet
For in front of me
Were many cars and vans
Spitting out bursts of grey smoke,
Into the gloom, dark clouds
Spread overhead.
The men inside the cars and vans
Were thoughtlessly littering bottles and cans.
There were no trees,
Flowers or anything green
Oh! What a horrible scene!

It was, I must say, with sadness and disgrace
The opposite of an eco-friendly place.

Out of nowhere there was an open archway,
With silvery grey and light green misty spirals,
Swirling inside the door.

'100 years in the future'
It said on the floor
I stepped inside
And landed somewhere
As I opened my eyes
I saw I was in a street,
And the sight I could see
Was very nice and sweet
For in front of me
There were joyful people walking
Not one car or van
And not one bottle or can
But there were trees so tall
It looked as if they were stitching Earth to the sky
The dazzling sun generously shone
Its bright rays to the people beneath.

Suddenly I was falling...
Falling into somewhere dark...

And as I landed with a thud
I'm sure it left a mark!
As I opened my eyes
I saw I was back in my bedroom
Then I leapt out of my bed
To make sure the dark gloomy scene
That I had just seen
Will always remain nothing more
Than just a dream
You can help too
You can make sure
That our Earth is always nice and green.

Tasnym Haque (10)
Fullwood Primary School, Barkingside

The Grey Bag Of Sounds

(Inspired by 'The Sound Collector' by Roger McGough)

A stranger called this morning dressed all in black and grey
Put every sound into a bag and carried them away.

The whistling of the kettle
The ticking of the clock
The turning of the lock
The purring of the kitten.

The popping of the toaster
The crunching of the flakes
When you spread the marmalade, the scraping noise it makes.

The hissing of the frying pan
The ticking of the grill
The bubbling of the bath tub as it starts to fill.

The crying of the baby,
The squeaking of the chair
The creaking of the stair
When you do the washing up, the gurgle of the drain

A stranger called this morning, left us only with no sounds.

Hania Akhtar (11)
Fullwood Primary School, Barkingside

Nightmare Unicorn

High above the clouds, all that I can see
Is a magical unicorn just for me.
I walk towards the unicorn,
But I soon see that it has gone.

All of a sudden, the sky turns dark,
I know that something bad will start.
I hear something move behind me
Which is actually very creepy!

Someone is coming, I better run,
This isn't a joke, I'm having no fun.
I wonder if the unicorn is evil,
And if it kills random people.

I see the unicorn coming with a knife,
I be very quiet and run to hide.
All I wish is to be in my bed,
I wake up having the feeling I slept well.

Zaynah Uddin (10)
Fullwood Primary School, Barkingside

The Child And The Fairies

The woods are full of fairies!
The trees are all alive.
The river overflows with them
See how they dip and dive!
What funny little follows
What dainty little dears!
They dance and leap, they prance and peep,
And utter fairy cheers.

I'd like to tame a fairy
To keep it on a shelf
To see it wash its little face
And dress its little self
Id' teach it pretty manners
It always should say 'Please'
And then you know I'd make it sew
And curtsy with its knees!

Disany Pirabaharan (10)
Fullwood Primary School, Barkingside

Pluto

I am a lonely planet
I am the smallest planet.

You may not know who I am
But the only friend I have is Charon
I am also the planet that doesn't follow the rules.

You may think that I am small
But I am something greater,

I am the reason my moon is famous
Charon adores me
Charon orbits me
And is a little smaller than me,

Charon and I have been orbiting each other forever
We twirl around on the orbit all the time
We never get dizzy.

Baraka Ahmed (10)
Fullwood Primary School, Barkingside

Dreamland

D ead tired, I lie asleep

R esting the body and soul

E ntering the land of dreams

A s fairies like twinkling stars, flutter gracefully and trees dance

M eanwhile luminous flowers bloom with glee

L ovelust is the unicorn whose hair gleams like the sun

A ll of a sudden, dark clouds cluster overlapping the enchanting sight

N ow this is happening, awakening me with a loud bang, my

D ream is over and I am all wrapped.

Imaan Atif (11)
Fullwood Primary School, Barkingside

Monsters Everywhere

Monsters everywhere
In the streets up the hill
Wherever you stare
They will breathe air.

Monsters everywhere
How can I escape?
My mind is so frightened
But my eyes are still awake.

Monsters everywhere
My heart's still pounding
This is so uncomfortable
Where on Earth am I standing?

Monsters everywhere
But yes, they're starting to go
I wake up on the floor
And don't know where to go.

Shreeya Gore (10)
Fullwood Primary School, Barkingside

Ghost

I can't tell you what I see,
I am as terrorised as can be,
The thunder ruling the sky,
And I am having the fate of being a passer-by.

Further and further I go,
He won't let go of me so,
Please someone get me out of here,
Trust me even the bravest would fear.

He hauls by the hair
But that's not fair!
Sometimes tears shed,
Soon I found out I'm awake in bed.

Mannan Arora (10)
Fullwood Primary School, Barkingside

Poor Little Unicorns

Unicorns fly,
Unicorns are high
Unicorns magic is glitzful
Come and make the glittering unicorns happy again

The poor little unicorns nothing to do,
Unicorns are unhappy without you
When the unicorns drift away,
You go find them and go with them.

Yippee the unicorns are happy again
'Cause of you they are happy
We made the unicorns happy again.

Miss Alyssa Ethridge (11)
Fullwood Primary School, Barkingside

Danger

I'm running down a corridor.
The corridor of an evil lair,
Knives getting thrown constantly,
Bullets spraying instantly.

The corridor starts to set fire,
I see the bottomless pit,
I know I am dead,
I jump in falling at light speed.

I open my eyes,
Thinking I'm in Heaven,
I'm actually in bed,
With my bed cover over my head.

Rocsan Robert-Chajee (11)
Fullwood Primary School, Barkingside

Meeting My Grandma Again

When my grandma died
I cried and cried
A few years later when I climbed a tree
I saw my grandma again, it was a mystery
She smiled at me
She was be able to see
I shrieked and shrieked
I freaked and freaked
I was as shocked at the notion
I told everyone all the information.

Mansi Gadhavi (11)
Fullwood Primary School, Barkingside

Once Upon A Dream

Once upon a dream, I awoke in a strange land
The sky was blue and I was too
It was colourful and bright, it was a delight
Until a great door appeared in front of me
I saw the Earth as small as a marble
I walked forward, but the door disappeared
There was nothing to be seen, until we meet again.

Aidan Gilbert (11)
Fullwood Primary School, Barkingside

Unicorn

Castle Corn
Let's have a ball
Flowers here and big and small
Unicorn want you to play.

So laugh and sing with us today
Unicorn, Unicorn where are you,
I want to play with you today.

I feel so sad I have to go home to bed
Sky blue, unicorn yellow.

Ria Singh (11)
Fullwood Primary School, Barkingside

My Puppy

When I go to bed
I curl up and rest my head,
My eyes close up
I think of a small pup
It lies in my hands
Day after day
I play.

My puppy grows
Day after day
It's my puppy's birthday
It's grown so big
Tonight I will sleep well.

Chiara Morante (11)
Fullwood Primary School, Barkingside

Unicorn In The Night Sky

I was standing in a magical land.
Then I saw a load of stars
They started to come together like Mars.
I saw it was a unicorn outline
So then I tried to run away but I wasn't going anywhere
But the unicorn got closer...
Suddenly it turned into a portal,
Then it started to pull me in
When I got through all I could see were
Loads and loads of unicorns
But everyone was just looking at one unicorn it was...
The outline unicorn, it was gigantic
It looked at me
Every little bit of her was falling apart
And all of it came to me
I was shocked, I was thinking it didn't like me
But it must have
Then all the other unicorns cheered for the thankfulness she gave us
But then they all prayed happily.

Amy Shepherd (9)
Heron Park Academy, Hampden Park

Tom Potter And The Dead Dreams Or Not

D own at my house I was practising my spells
E xpeliarmus was one
A portal came in my face to show I'm in a race
D own at the start line I was wasting time

D an Wicks was running as fast as he could stand
R ussell kicked him and then he was banned
E than was punched into a river
A dam ate too much chicken liver
M olly was as slow as a snail
S ally was all covered in freezing hail

O man was so close to the trophy
R ound the bend he was pushed, that was Sophie

N orman fell down at the last hurdle
O liver won the race but I was close behind
T ut-tut Oliver won sausages that were rotten.

Zaq Villegas (9)
Heron Park Academy, Hampden Park

The Bananas Take Over!

B ananas are evil and will take over
A ndy is the banana king
N athan is slow but he's strong as well
A nd the bananas' favourite food is banana
N aughty bananas want to take over
A nd they have an army, you will die
S adly they have taken over

A ll that's left is bananas
R emember don't trust bananas
E ven if they look tasty

E at something other than bananas
V ery naughty bananas
I hate bananas
L onely forever because of bananas.

Patryk Przemyslaw Galon (9)

Heron Park Academy, Hampden Park

Famous Unicorn Fly

F lutter like a butterfly
A ngry like a tiger
M annequin challenge
O lly the penguin
U pset unicorns everywhere
S unny like summer

U pset like winter
N ot afraid
I gnore the bullies
C olourful like a rainbow
O range is your favourite
R uns like a cheetah
N ot so sad if she's happy

F lapping wings in the sky
L ike a butterfly
Y ou and I in the sky.

Summer Tomlinson (9)
Heron Park Academy, Hampden Park

Lost In The Galaxy

G ale got lost in the galaxy
A t the spaceship there was no help
L ater Buster the dog came
A t last the spaceship door opened
X mas Day is only two days away
Y ellow planet got hit by a laser

B uster tried to stop it but he didn't
O nly one planet got hit
Y elled his mum to wake up

M agic things on Mars
A liens destroying a bus on Mars
R eally dangerous
S ignature gone wrong.

Tariq Houri (8)
Heron Park Academy, Hampden Park

The Wizard

W hizzing past the magical forest
 I nto the shining river
 Z ooming past the wizards
 A mazing magic sparkling by
 R aining magical dust
 D ashing through sparkles

W izards spraying sparkles
 I cing in lightning
 T hrough thunder
 H iding behind magic dust

M aking magic from dust
 A mazing magic
 G athering magic dust
 I ce through fire
 C asting in fire.

Samir Jurgelas (9)
Heron Park Academy, Hampden Park

33

Magical Land

M agical ocean
A cloud puffed like candyfloss
G reat to go on holiday
I ce is very cold
C ream is yummy for everyone
A magical sun is so bright in the sky
L and is beautiful

L ike dancing people love is very nice
A nd my eyes are shining from the magic
N o one will find how to be magical
D iamonds are very shiny.

Selina Tison (8)
Heron Park Academy, Hampden Park

A Happy Holiday

Here I am in the plane
Going as fast as a droplet of rain
On the beach in the sun
Playing with my toy gun
Buying ice cream, it's as cold
As a freezing lump of coal.
At night I went to the opera
It was louder than Mrs Singing Doctor
Then I went home to bed
Ready for the next day ahead
But the next day it was raining
So I had to go home.

Alfie Moore (9)
Heron Park Academy, Hampden Park

Up To Orion

S pace is the floating
P lanets
A star
C ome to space and float
E scape the world

O n the moon
R ound space
I love space
O rion
N ight

M oon is bright
O ver the clouds
O ff the train
N o gravity.

Zayn Wood (9)
Heron Park Academy, Hampden Park

Candy World!

C ome back, let me eat you Candy
A pple flavoured lollipop, yum-yum
N ot enough chocolate
D ripping chocolate
Y ummy!

W hat nice sweets
O h so yummy
R umbling in my tummy
L ollipop
D one, not yet... more candy!

Amy Gough (8)
Heron Park Academy, Hampden Park

The Best Dream Ever

My friends hate bats
They love hats
I hate hats
I love bats
We're not the same
But we're in the game.

I'm a bit weird
But I have a fear
My friends have fear
But they're not weird.

Your cheeks are like roses
And I like poses.

Bethany Fitches (9)
Heron Park Academy, Hampden Park

Fairy Land

F airies are kind
A nd fairies flutter
I magination is great here
R uby my other friend
Y ummy, yummy porridge

L ola is my pet rabbit
A na is Olivia's pet
N othing is better
D iscover Fairy Land.

Felicity Russell (9)
Heron Park Academy, Hampden Park

Wizardry

W izards fighting
 I magination in the castle
Z ombies take over
A mazing magic
R emaining wizards
D angerous wizards.

Dexter Allen (8)
Heron Park Academy, Hampden Park

The Sugar Dance

As I awoke from my slumber,
I stumbled up in a lumber,
I was blinded by sugar sweets,
With tummy-filling treats.

Unicorns and all,
While glitter trees stood tall,
Lollipops danced,
I didn't think it was a trance.

Sugar plum fairies flew,
Past some honey dew,
As I lunged,
Chocolate bars sung.

I collected some treats,
I sat down on a seat,
As dawn steered near,
When my eyes began to close with a tear.

Charlee King (9)
Kingswood Primary School, Basildon

A Tale Of Time

When I was 18, I made a time machine,
I tested it with my friend,
We went to the year 3876,
After night had ended forever.

I saw flying knights fighting,
And dragons and knights falling,
I saw a castle, 'Shelter!' I did shout,
The castle looked like a super old church.

Bang! Shouted the doors as I opened them,
And saw the candlelight dance,
I saw something shiny,
I tentatively walked over to it.

My friend ran over,
It was labelled 'Elytra',
We thought it was some armour that was completely
blown over,
I put it on...

Whoosh! I flew in the air,
I grabbed a hovering sword,
I flew outside and saw a bear,
I started to fight and get quite bored.

After ten hours of fighting we went using a bus,
Back to the time machine's dusty door,
Back to 2027,
Bringing the Elytra with us.

We saw lots of people,
Wearing suits and dresses,
'Hooray!' they shouted. 'It worked!'
After 9 years of time travelling I become famous, and
have a room of successes.

Oliver James Clegg (8)

Priory Primary School, Bicknacre

Wonderland

Pixies flying on unicorns, fairies sitting on
marshmallows,
Fairies flying with chocolate coins, unicorns galloping in
chocolate clouds,
While rose red roses dance in the air.
I'm really, really excited.

Green trees wave as the sparkling unicorns snore,
Mushroom houses shimmer,
While baby trees start dancing with the rose-red roses,
The chocolate clouds start raining your favourite
sweets.

Birds start singing 'Tweet, tweet!'
While they sing they turn bright blue like a first
morning cloud,
The flowing river suddenly turns half gold and half see-
through,
Suddenly, fairies jump into the river
Kaboom! They all jump in.
Elves start doing starfish jumps in the grass.

The boiling sun suddenly smiles at me while winking quickly,
Butterflies start doing cartwheels in the air,
While baby unicorns are galloping and learning how to fly.
Then I wake up and see a mushroom near my bed.

Georgia Whitehead (7)

Priory Primary School, Bicknacre

Football Match

Once upon a dream,
When I was fast asleep,
A dream popped into my head,
It was football.

I was on the 3D Arsenal pitch,
Arsenal vs Watford.
The stadium was buzzing with people.
Bang! Against the fence. *Crash!*

Wayne Rooney with 150 goals.
I was Messi with 149 goals.
It was the cup final.
The trophy was like a pot of gold.

I was with my teammates.
I was a superior striker.
Our team were feeling confident against Watford,
It started, I scored a goal in 10 minutes.

Next it was half-time.
After the team came out I smashed the bar, *crash!*
I scored a goal from 35 yards out.
The whistle blew like a lion roaring.

Arsenal were the champions.
I was the record breaker.
The shiny trophy was mine.
Bump! I was back in my glorious bed.

Sam Brooks (7)
Priory Primary School, Bicknacre

Will My Dream Come True?

Will my dream come true?
I write my dream and say goodnight,
Then go to my sleeping bed,
I fall asleep and dream about my mysterious dream,
I am astonished and go through a door,
I am in Dreamland!

There are gorgeous trees which grow presents and
sweet things too,
The ground is made of soft sweets,
It's just as I'd written it!
I find some flowers that smell of honey,
And find some animals that have wings too!

Then I fly around on my wings that are as delicate as
silk,
Then find a crying wand in my hair,
Tinkle, tinkle.
I use my wand to make some magic,
And I magic up a dancing candle, it dances all around
me.

Suddenly I awake in my bed,
I find the wand still in my hair,
Then I think my dream is really real,
But I keep it as a secret.
Will my dream come true?

Elizabeth Cook (7)
Priory Primary School, Bicknacre

The Magical Day

A little girl was in bed,
Waiting for her dream to pop up in her head,
Finally it arrived.

I went through a magical door,
Instantly, I was greeted by a bear,
'Hello,' he said trying to wiggle his paw.

This is the land of rabbits and bears,
Let's take you and Teddy on an adventure,
Just you wait and see.

We went away to see a rabbit,
She was so kind, you wouldn't even know it,
She was drawing a magnificent picture,
Her name was Rara, she was coming on our adventure.
Teddy and I had such incredible fun,
But now it was time to go,
It was hard to say goodbye, but we were fine.

When I woke up I was as snuggled as could be,
I was hugging Teddy tightly,
Wow, that was only a dream!

Teddy and I can't wait for another magical adventure.

Charlotte Sophia Merrifield (7)
Priory Primary School, Bicknacre

Galaxy World Dreamland

G loom! Where am I? A beautiful, colourful land

A rgh! A galaxy world is sucking me up!

L ook! It has a lot of floating stars hovering around

A h-ha! I can float and I feel like an amazing bird

X ylophones playing on a huge galaxy planet as big as the world

Y es, I would like to go back to the normal world now

L ots of smells of chocolate fill the air. I can't air anything

A ll I see is a gargantuan galaxy background with white stars

N ice world but I want to go back home now

D ash back to my comfortable bed

Let's get back to another astounding dream.

Daniella Maria Waterhouse (7)
Priory Primary School, Bicknacre

Rome

I went to Rome in a dangerous dome and bought a
fiery comb,
After the embarrassed king came,
The gladiator school took me in, so I trained hard.
It smelled like a trench, gladiators hit tens and nines.
I fought like a hero and almost lost my brain.
I killed Caesar Augustus in the biggest battle in the
entire world.

Suddenly I ruled Rome and built an army dome,
The dome was snoring and was boring,
Next, pop! An angel appeared, silky wings behind it,
Lightheartedly, I climbed on its back and it floated like
a hoverboard.

Bang! I appeared in my silk like bed.

Kaboom! My dog Diddy appeared on my head,
He cuddled me like my mum.

Enrico Barbosa (8)
Priory Primary School, Bicknacre

Dreamland

D ragons and spiders crawl in the night.

R oughly getting out of the web that the spider spun.

E very one eating sweets and chocolate.

A unicorn escaped from the web too.

M y unicorn and fairy are safe and sound.

L ong dragons snarling in the cave.

A ll evil about to eat the fairy while the cauldron bubbles pop.

'N o!' I shouted raging like a rhino into the dark, gloomy cave.

D ragons fly up, up and up into the sky afraid of me.

'Bye-bye,' I say as I am waving my seriously strawberry lace sword and chocolate shield.

Ambrielle Lawrenson (7)
Priory Primary School, Bicknacre

Nightmare

N ever shall I be ready for this time

I find a group of spiders and ghosts

G hosts with only a face and lightning in rain clouds

H ard bricks fly in my eye

T he spiders use their silky webs to shut the door

M ummy ghosts make booing, shrieking sounds in my face

A nd the daddy-long-legs fly like an angry dragon

R ain, thunder lightning strike above my head. I am as scared as a baby elephant

E verything goes pitch-black and suddenly I noticed I'm back in my beautiful bed.

Jake Jehan (8)
Priory Primary School, Bicknacre

Frightmare

F uriously I land on the moon by bus

R ight at the side of the crater a door lay

I enter, I see the blue beast

G etting our swords out we hear

H alf the aliens fire their arrows

T en swords as sharp as a tooth sway swiftly through the air

M ighty cheese falls from the moon, *kaboom!*

A storm starts to roar

R avenous arrows fly around like a flock of birds

E lectrical thunder about to strike

S uddenly I wake up with the curtains running from the window.

Alex Drane (8)

Priory Primary School, Bicknacre

Dreamland

D iving metal parts from iron clouds.
R obots flying around the powerful city.
E very house is made out of razor-sharp sparks.
A nd food is made out of chocolate.
M agic monsters boom like rockets.
L egs are tooth brushes for brushing your teeth.
A luminium pets clatter their tails together.
N ever give up at robot school.
D evils coming from robot playgrounds.

We can defeat them nothing will stop us.

Finley Beattie (8)
Priory Primary School, Bicknacre

Dream Land

D reams pass by making wishes come true.

R aging rabbits magically pass by.

E ating lovely, sweet marshmallows.

A chocolate fountain was filling the pond up.

M agic candyfloss hovers by.

L arge sweet smells goes along.

A huge loud sound leads me to a magical house.

N obody knows it is dream land.

D isappointment when I woke up. It was just a dream.

Lucas Cross (7)
Priory Primary School, Bicknacre

Frosty Winter's Morning

Frost like sugar
Bushes like big cakes
Birds swooping
Playing 'It'.
Bare trees are skeletons
Ivy climbing up them.
Flowers with frost on top
Are like lollipops,
Up in the blue sky
Clouds are pillows
I dream of summer.

Joe Finan (9)
St Andrew's CE Primary School, Nuthurst

Volcano Adventures

V olcano had been watched this misty, rainy night

O n the landing, in my bed and mum turned off the light

L acking concentration, daytime was in a lock

C lashing reality and dreams, I fell on a rock

A mazing tech in a volcano

N early stubbing my toe

O n the edge of the lava hole

A nnoying little rock guardians with wands made out of coal

D readfully, dangerous rock demon came out of some ashes

V oid of water, in we go for lava monster lashes

E ventually, we reach the bottom so the guardians pulled some levers

N ow we go shooting back out, looking sensible as beavers

T ragically, the guardians go shooting on the edge

U nexpectedly, one of the wands lands just on the ledge

R earing up, I fired a spell right into the monster's mouth

E xactly as expected he flew up and shot south

S uddenly, I woke up to find myself myself lying with my brother, Ralf.

Daniel Selden (9)
St Michael's Junior School, Galleywood

The Saviour Of Dream World

A bleeding star passes through the sky,
Mighty kings watch down from up high.
Their wrinkled foreheads crease in thought,
Choosing a hero to defeat the forces that have brought
Fear throughout the peaceful night,
And defeat to the heroic knights.
Their withered faces light up with joy
As a young child leaves safety to retrieve her toy.
At last a hero has been found
Suddenly an ear-piercing shriek echoes around.

Five years on, she is still alive,
Being taught how to fight and how to survive.
The evil queen is still in power,
Hiding at the top of an ancient tower.
But her dark reign will end soon
And Dream World will return by the light of the moon.

The clock strikes midnight and the silver moon glows,
The child enters the icy tower, shivering from her head
to toes.
Fear courses through her veins but she continues to
climb,
At the top of the stairs she encounters a sleeping
guard in time.

With a click of her fingers and a stamp of her foot,
The door flies open revealing a room engulfed in soot.
The evil queen lays cackling in her sleep,
She knows the deed must be done before Dream World
is awoken by the sheep.
Banished magical creatures arise from hiding after
years of threat,
Hissing and snorting ready to attack anything it meets.
The ominous night sky changes from indigo to red,
And the grass becomes emerald green, finally people
can rest in bed.
The evil queen is finally dead
'Our hero must be a god,' dreamers said.

I do not remember much of the life-changing night,
Nor do I remember the heroic fight.
As you may have guessed, I am part of the dream,
Now promise me you will not scream;
For I am the hero who was chosen by kings of old,
And now my tale of defeating the queen has been told.
Be thankful for everything you receive
But remember you can do anything if you believe.

Abbie Rogers (10)
St Michael's Junior School, Galleywood

Toy Land!

I was in Toyland
The toys were at my command.
They were moving very fast.
One toy had a hat, another was a cat.
I carried the toys around
They made such a sound,
They woke the toy snake
He was mad.
He chased the knight
They had a fight.
I crept away with the other toys
I told them not to make a noise.
The toys said, 'We're sorry, we wanted to cheer
We didn't want anyone to disappear!'
I said, 'Please don't do it again
You might wake the hen.
The other toys will disappear to somewhere else
They don't know
Into a distant land nobody knows!'
We walked to a toy lake
We met Mrs Snake
She said, 'I'm making a race
Would you like to participate?'
Everyone said, 'Yes!'

To show they are the best
It was like a big test.
We were at the starting line
Ready to shine. 1, 2, 3... go!
Running just like we should,
We were jumping over stone then - thud!
I fell in mud.
But that wasn't going to stop me from finishing the game
I got back up again
I said to myself, 'hoe... log... wall... dodge small... wall!'
I was nearly there
Beside me was a ballerina
I wanted to win
I didn't want to lose
I didn't want to hear boos.
I was trying my hardest
I was running my fastest
The ballerina fell in some mud
With a thud
I cross the finish line
I won at last
The big trophy went to me
I was very pleased - whoopee!

Rhianna Dunkley (10)
St Michael's Junior School, Galleywood

The Wembley Dream

I tightly tied my laces so my boots would stay on,
The coach braced us for the team talk,
We were to play against our all-time rivals,
I pulled up my captain's armband with pride.

The huge tunnel echoed with chants,
Vigorously the opponents scowled at me,
Loudly the ominous sounding crowd welcomed us,
We quickly took our positions.

To start the game we had won kick-off,
Swiftly the ball rolled on the flat grass,
It came to my direction,
The game had begun.

Crunching tackles flew, shin pads cracked,
Yellow filled the air,
Red emerged, eleven became ten,
Anger added to the air,
Will this give us more of a chance?

Not much time to go,
A spiralling ball across the pitch,
My foot stretched towards the sky,
Stuck to my foot like glue,
My sight was set on goal.

Defender rapidly running,
Time running out,
Crowd roaring like fighting lions,
My heart pumping like a piston.

I shoot for the top corner,
Keeper leaping heroically,
Nervous faces,
Will it go in?

The net waves welcoming the ball,
A spread of happiness appeared,
Joyful faces, mixed emotions,
'Goal!'

Sound of the whistle echoed around the stadium,
I can barely walk,
Climbing the stairs with pride,
Lifting the heavy silver cup
We are the champions, but is it a dream?

Harry Jacobs (10)
St Michael's Junior School, Galleywood

Creepy, Eerie, Nightmarish Thoughts!

O n my comfortable bed my eyes feel heavy, all of a sudden I fell fast asleep

N ow I've realised I am having a nightmare, as I can see bright orange flames dancing

C olossal, hairy spiders stalking their prey and eerie alabaster-white, laughing clowns

E verywhere I look and go, creepy things stalk.

U nderground I hear macabre monsters calling for me

P ushing towards me, the ebony black shadows come ever nearer

O ver my head the reluctant ravens sing a horrible tune

N ever have I seen so many freaky, revolting animals.

A most horrible sight is when you see a gruesome ghoul devour its prey

D emons suck the blood from its weak helpless food

R avenous vampires hunting down into vulnerable food sources

E ndless, this most frightening dream is endless

A ll over I want this to be

M y palms are sweating when I awake.

Christopher Daly (10)
St Michael's Junior School, Galleywood

New York's Creepy Alley

N obody dares to enter this alley but I do
E verybody disagrees with me
W hilst I say, 'Why shouldn't you?'

Y et I do not understand
O rdinary, it cannot be
R eady for something to come out the land
K nowing what will come, I will see
S piders will be listening for me

C reepy spiders coming out the ground
R apidly speeding outwards
E very spider making lots of sound
E ven if I cry it will not kill the king spider
P roceeding to wait, I was thirsty so where's the cider
Y oung dino appears and vanishes

A dorable dinos came to save the world
L uckily a fight
L ast of the spiders died and Dino said
'E verybody
Y ou're home safe in bed.'

Lucas Marsh (10)
St Michael's Junior School, Galleywood

The Coal Cat

Dong... It's the grandfather clock
I check the door's lock
The water on my bedside table tinkles like a wind chime
The moon rises to my window, midnight time
The slanted tiles on the roof shudder, then...
My nightmare begins all over again.
A billowing plume of jet-black soot,
Plummets down the chimney chute
The embers in the fireplace smoulder
Lamp-like eyes as round as a boulder.
Whiskers like moonbeams as wicked as knives
Claws like iron, as curved as scythes
This feline ferocity glides onto the floor
His lustrous gaze turns to my bedroom door
My body is frozen, I try to hide
My mouth is silent, I'm screaming inside.
A rumbling purr,
As soft as his fur before
He slinks to the doorway
And I saw...
Dong... The clocks strikes one
And Coal Cat is gone.

Evan Flack (11)
St Michael's Junior School, Galleywood

The Doors To Dreamland!

Stars glisten in the sky,
Faces awestruck as it passes by,
One moment only is it clear,
That the door to Dreamland was getting near.

No one knows what lies inside,
What the doors to Dreamland are trying to hide,
Cotton candy clouds could it be,
Or maybe a raging mulberry sea?

Could there be witches stirring potions,
Wild beasts causing commotions?
How about roses reaching to the sky,
Little humming birds singing lullabies?

Do superheroes rule the land,
Living in houses posh and grand?
Maybe it's a place where evils roam?
Could it be a place mythical creatures call home?

No one knows what lies inside,
What the doors to Dreamland are trying to hide,
Humans have never been to this world,
Too scared of what might be unfurled.

Olivia Davanzo (11)
St Michael's Junior School, Galleywood

Clown Town's Real!

C ans clattering below on the floor

L ying low in a hospital bed so poor

O utside stood a sign saying Clown Town Beware!

W addling closer was a small clown saying, 'Don't you dare!'

N ot a second wasted as the clocks we're bare

T ick-tock, tick-tock the clocks went on the clowns

O nly the bodies were still

W hy was I put in Clown Town?

N oises ran through my mind... which clown had the crown?

S uddenly a night fury but the colour was brown!

R andom clowns popped their heads out of the top trees,

E veryone loves the breeze

A ll I could think of was shelter, and then I saw a helter-skelter

L ying on the floor was my favourite teacher but she was a clown.

Hannah Samuels (10)
St Michael's Junior School, Galleywood

The Whale And I

Last night when I was tucked up tight in bed,
I visited an ocean land deep in my head,
An underwater paradise just waiting to be discovered,
Now I have found it, it's finally uncovered.

The rippling current of the exotic sea,
Wraps around my swirling body,
As I speedily swim through the ocean,
The fish try and copy my twirling motion.

Out of the corner of my eye,
I spot a mighty blue whale passing by,
The whale is the leader of its extraordinary kind,
With superior power bursting out and fear hidden deep
inside.

He wants to have friends just like you and I
But his isn't very brave, he is rather shy,
Every day when I look up to the ebony night sky,
I think of the adventures I have has with my friend,the
whale, at night.

Bobbi Lyla Brook (11)
St Michael's Junior School, Galleywood

The General Of Racing

As I left the garage in my Mustang
I was heading towards the race track.
When I turned up at the race track
Somebody was asking people to race
So me and my friend said we would race him.

Then me and my friend lined up at the starting line.
On your marks, get set, go
We sped down the track
And just then a ramp car hit my friend's car and flipped
him over
I watched him die.
I went home in tears.

After a while of being vulnerable
I got up and started to finish the car I was building.
When I finished all I had to do was paint it
And give it a horn.

The next day I went to the final race
Three... two... one... Go
We were going at speed
I just saw the ramp car
So I drove on two wheels and won!

Alfie Palmer (10)
St Michael's Junior School, Galleywood

Daydreamers...

A glistening flash of gold,
A story never to be told,
A quick dash of blue - ever so true,
A graceful sprinkle of red - to tuck you into bed,
And then a long view of paradise.

A shiny crimson sea - busy as a bee,
Fresh iridescent grass - clear as a shard of glass
An opal flicker of sky - with birds flying high
Sun-glazed mango trees - bringing you to your knees,
Hypnotising you to follow them through this world.

The one I never liked - always leading me on this hike,
This dream is imprisoning, it's so threatening,
A menacing rosy pink - scarring me with ink,
Can I ever escape the constraining rose-gold tape,
Or will I be a minion - never giving my opinion...

Joely Lovett (10)
St Michael's Junior School, Galleywood

I'm Going On Holiday!

We're going on holiday
We are going by car
I wanted to go by plane
It wasn't that far.

We are going on the motorway
That I really hate
With all these cars pushing past us
We are going to be late!

We are finally here
I must go to sleep
But I am too excited
So to the window I creep.

And I stare at a beautiful sight
That I have just seen
A sandy golden beach
That's impeccably clean.

And after all this
I go back to bed
With plenty of satisfaction
Right there in my head.

I wake up in the morning,
I open my eyes
I go outside and
Look up to the blue skies.

Alexandra Bacon (9)
St Michael's Junior School, Galleywood

The Several Eyes

T he water streaming
H earing something fleeing
E very step I was regretting

S uddenly, a giant dark tree came in front of me
E very step I took several eyes appeared on the giant dark tree
V ery lethargically I stepped away
E laborate eyes coming closer to me
R apidly I tripped I couldn't see...
A t first I heard a scatter of branches
L ong beady eyes staring at me

E very one of the eyes came out of the tree
Y es, I was trapped, the eyes turned cream
E ventually, I woke up and it was just a silly dream
S afe in my bed and so I was relieved.

Leon Kuhanuka (9)
St Michael's Junior School, Galleywood

Alfie The Great

A lfie (that's me) was on a deserted island because I got captured and put in a cannon and blasted to the island

L ost

F orever

I was petrified, worried and curious that the island was so small

E ast Island. I thought I knew where I was

'I s that a coconut,' I said to myself, 'I'll get it'

S ea rattled like something was coming

G rabbed it

R an to the tree and smashed it wide open

E at, *yum-yum*

A pirate came and saved me

T reasure, he saw. The pirate said, 'That's my booty and let him have some and took him home.

Alfie James England (10)

St Michael's Junior School, Galleywood

The Clouds Adventure

I was lifted late one night
High into the clouds
All around like candyfloss
I started to leap around.

Unexpectedly my funny friends appeared
And they hopped around with me
I hopped away to hide amongst the cotton clouds
While Millia strode off to seek
After a while we lay to rest, to eat the clouds
Flavours, the yummy flavours, strawberry, raspberry and mint.

We searched out a rainbow to go back home
The colours, the lovely colours
Pretty unicorns were flying beside us
All their different colours were lovely
After a while the amazing dream was sadly over
The call of Mum, 'Time to go!'

Jessica Merrifield (8)
St Michael's Junior School, Galleywood

The Mysterious Jungle

Once upon a dream
My friends and I had an exciting sleepover
We sneaked out into the starry night
Through the foggy jungle we explored.

We saw a wooden bridge in the distance
Suddenly we saw a clown appear
His face was pale and he was holding red and black balloons.

I tripped and... *bang!*
I hit my head on a rock
A loud scream awoke me
In my hospital bed surrounded by Ewoks
My heart was pounding a hundred times a second

I hear footsteps coming towards me
Laughter surrounding my ears
My head spins and my eyes begin to open
I look around and the terrifying clown is near.

Ethan Samuels (9)
St Michael's Junior School, Galleywood

Dreams Are Like A Story

A dream is like a story,
From nightmares to fame and rags to riches and
luxurious glory.
You could be a princess locked in a tower so high
Or just a plain palace with turrets reaching to the sky.
You could have a nightmare of ghosts, witches, and
vampires or of trolls
Mixing you in their human stew.
Don't forget the crazy dreams they're the best for sure
To your own food talking or eating toast on the rocky
shore.
You could dream about being in the best movie ever,
Or flying to Neverland, where you grow up, never!
Dreams are special, all of them tell a story
So don't be afraid to sleep and witness a dream's
glory.

Hope Abigail Burchell (11)
St Michael's Junior School, Galleywood

Football Poem

The stars were bright
At the middle of the night
I was asleep
Dreaming deep
I dreamed of being a football player
But one day the sky got greyer
It started to rain
I was filled with pain
We slowly walked towards our manager
Because there was so much danger
This was he worst day I ever had
Because I was really sad
I remembered this day when I was sixteen
It was even worse than when I was fifteen
On the next day I played another match
My dad told me to not give up and don't get sad
I enjoyed it so much because I scored so many goals
My dad took me to the crystal shop to buy some
special stones.

Louis Roberts (8)
St Michael's Junior School, Galleywood

The Game Of Chess

I open my eyes, I see black and white
As white as snow as black as night
Looks familiar, but I can't remember
Like the game of chess last September.

I look around me, what do I see?
Millions of chessmen, just like me.
Now I realise where I am
Now it hits me with a bam!

Frantic and puzzled, I hear a voice,
'Go to A4!' do I have a choice?
A freezing hand gripped me
Oh please, let me be!

'Your turn!' I hear the voice cry,
I try to move, I really try,
Then I wake up, bored as can be
I'm playing chess and everyone's trying to wake me!

Shweta Sharma (10)
St Michael's Junior School, Galleywood

Flying Zombies!

I woke up this morning in my bed,
I looked out the window and saw things ahead,
I wondered what they were?
'Let's go out and see,'
And I realised that they were flying zombies
Flying everywhere, it really scared me,
Backing into a corner, they are surrounding me
I shouted for help as I need it right now
Coming towards me without a doubt,
Screaming in horror were zombies looking at me
But really is was just a dream?
I explained to them and they said, 'Stop going on!'
I guess this was my dream about flying zombies
I hope you enjoyed this amazing dream.

Chloe Rose Taylor (11)
St Michael's Junior School, Galleywood

Rainbow Unicorn Land

R unning above the clouds, the ones that are as white as snow

A nd trees that are made of candyfloss

I n Rainbow Unicorn Land, I can be the first to say whoa

N ow I am the boss

B oss of riding a unicorn

O nce biting a piece of candy, yum!

W ill it grow back? Will it be reborn?

U nicorn Land, it will stay here forever,

N ever will it go

I magine if this nature would never

C ome again, what a blow

O nly I can dream this dream

R unning above the clouds

N ow never let me wake up from my unicorn team.

Layla Grace McClean (10)
St Michael's Junior School, Galleywood

The Future Awaits

Sitting in the back of a wondrous machine,
Waving goodbye to the glorious queen,
Oh no, oh ho! A terrible problem has begun
As the machine hissed and puffed and started to run,
Faster and quicker, darting and breaking
The pressure expanding and creating,
A sickly feeling down below,
As the broken machine started to slow,
In AD thirty thousand and twenty-four
This is where the time-rift tore
Ha-ha! Hey-hey!
This bad boy is coming to play
In a future city, held aloft by clouds
And quite a few humiliating sounds
Relaxed forever, lazing away
In my head
Lying in bed.

Daniel Hudson (10)
St Michael's Junior School, Galleywood

Best Footballer In The World

The green pitch as green as a fresh leaf swishing and swashing in the wind.
The heavy goal post on the pitch and the shiny boots standing out.

The goalkeeper's gloves hard as a bat. No mud on the pitch.
So happy but when it rains the horror is back out. The best in the world Ronaldo's boot is so hard it can slice a brick.

F antastic football
O ut into the pitch
O ut into the goal
T ime is running better start scoring
B all in the air
A ir floating briskly
L ook at the ball
L ook where you can pass.

Lewis Powell (9)
St Michael's Junior School, Galleywood

Paralysed

Drifting off in a nervous daze
Eyes heavy and closing.

A breath, a warm breath of a wild striped animal
A tiger, a beast,
Close, too close
Legs paralysed, shut down not working.

Meandering in a marine world of teeming life,
Then a swish of a tail, a snap of jaws,
Something was lurking in the depths of the ocean,
A flash of ivory white teeth, a sparkle of scales,
A shark, a monster
Close, too close
Arms, legs paralysed, shut down not working.

A pit, a deep pit,
Falling, falling fast
Then a jolt
Awake,
Alive.

Oscar Harverson (11)
St Michael's Junior School, Galleywood

Monster Night

M idnight it is, so dark and gloomy
O ver the hill I hear a moan and groan
N ever did this space feel so roomy
S uddenly I heard the crunch of bone
T hen I heard a shout and scream from the hill
E choes from the scream I shivered
R unning I should but instead I stand still

N ight gets lighter, I become more brave
I can now see what made me so scared
G rey squirrels eating nuts on the waste bin
'H ello,' I muttered to the squirrels loud
T hey seem like they knew what I was saying.

James White (9)
St Michael's Junior School, Galleywood

Happy Turns To Sad ~ Dream Turns To Nightmare!

D ragons fly around me creating shapes in their smoke,

R eality is far behind me so I relax and watch mystical folk,

E very fantasy is becoming real,

A nd my house is made of chocolate

M oreover I am happy, as happy as I can be!

W hat's this? A huge, dark cloud starts to spread

O ver my dreamworld; my happiness is dead

R ampaging trolls knock over my chocolate house

L ava goes everywhere, consequently I am terrified

D estruction reigns but then I wake up - it really was just a dream...

Ruth Selden (11)
St Michael's Junior School, Galleywood

The Hungry Games Catching Pants On Fire

I am Fatniss Everdeen

Are you a friend or are you a foe?
Are you hiding my hot dog roll?
Behind my back, lying flat I sniff you out,
You smell like a flapjack.

Lying down low, the sniper awaits
But all I can think about is winning the strawberry cake.

I know who you are Tofu-Rue
Come out, come out! I'm hungry for you!
I get out my spaghetti bow
Shooting meatballs of fire, across the dome.

Ah-ha, victory as she drops dead -
She'll taste good with a slab of bread tonight.

Joseph Nicholls (10)
St Michael's Junior School, Galleywood

Untitled

As I see stars glowing as bright as a lantern
What was flickering, I step into a macabre gritty horizon
As I take one more step I realise it's a beautiful land
I see a prowling lion but everything else is bland
As I get closer he says hello
What was that noise?
It must have been a hippo swooshing his nose
I glance and glance right, suddenly I get a fright
As I turn around there's no need to fear
It as just an elephant playing with my ear
I jumped on top of the elephant's back
He gave me a ride to see the wonderful lion pride.

Noah Amir Taylor (10)
St Michael's Junior School, Galleywood

Superheroes!

Superheroes are number one
And they have so much fun
Their job is the best
Guess what, it beats the rest.

They have powers that go bang
Every day we want to play
But they're off saving the day

If you had one wish
It should be to be a superhero
You can be a super kid
And have the best gadgets

If I were you, I would fly like an angel
And invisibility so you can creep up on baddies
You will be the coolest kid in town
Don't forget superheroes, never give up!

Ruby Carroll (8)
St Michael's Junior School, Galleywood

Ready For A Win

R e-doing our great tactics
E veryone listening
A nd ready for loads of kicks
D own the tunnel we line up
Y et our opponent is top of the league

F atigue our coach is,
O h bless the lord that we win
R eferee blows his whistle, whilst the evil sky hangs above

A s the match kicks off whilst angry clouds rain

W hen it finished the score was 3-2 to us
I nto the tunnel we skipped
N ormally this would be a loss.

Harry Brown (9)
St Michael's Junior School, Galleywood

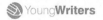
Once Upon A Detrimental Dream

It all started that very night,
Be warned this poem will give you a fright.

It was a cold and stormy night,
Where the night sky had no light.
The ominous black clouds came rolling on
All houses were murky, gloomy and dim.

Boom! Crash! Thunder roars
The wind so powerful, pulling off doors,
Bang! Crack! Lightning clatters down,
I look out the window to see my neighbour's dog drown,
The rain came plummeting down,
Evil eyes stared out of the mist, followed by a frown.

Beth Kirk (10)
St Michael's Junior School, Galleywood

Night-Time Fears

As I lie here in my bed
My heart is filling with dread
I can feel my eyes beginning to close
The coldness is spreading from my head to my toes
And now my imagination has come to life
It's as clear and sharp as the end of a knife
I'm in a field where everything is grey
In a place where skeletons lay
But then out of the shadows
Comes a huge scary clown
Upon its face is a big, grumpy frown
Then as the clown looms over me
And I'm screaming with fright
Mummy comes in and turns on the light.

Lola Flack (8)
St Michael's Junior School, Galleywood

Dark Dreams

It was midnight, things appeared
This was exactly what I feared,
The sky was dark
I saw a black mark
Painted on the bloodshot sky,
There was a note but who was it by?
'I will get you,' it said,
Why was I not in bed?

It was midnight, no light
This gave me a fright,
Eerie sounds and creepy clowns,
Turned my smile upside down,
I curled up into a ball
To hide from the creatures that did crawl
Something dripped on my head
I reached out and it was red!

Emily Kerwin (10)
St Michael's Junior School, Galleywood

Magical Minecraft

Where am I? A jungle
I can hear a rumble
Lightning, crackle bang, fire in the jungle
Run away without a fumble.

Tomorrow I will build my house
Try and be as quiet as a mouse
Chop down wood, get some food.

I need to get some rest
But these zombies are a pest
We can't go to the Nether yet
Because we haven't slept yet.

It's exhausting at the Nether
Floating as light as a feather
The fire-breathing Ender Dragon
I shout as scary as a Kraken.

Raffael Ollivier (8)
St Michael's Junior School, Galleywood

Horror House

H eaving off the sheet of my bed
O uch! I landed on my head
R otating my head, I see a black figure,
R eady to attack, the figure comes closer
O nly me, no one to see
R apidly I blink, the figure can no longer be seen

H aving heart racing, as I search
O n the window I see blood
U nderneath me I could see
S omething the size of a flood, couldn't hear because
of a scream
E dging off my bed, I wake up.

Ashton Scott (10)
St Michael's Junior School, Galleywood

Found/Lost

F orever I've been trapped in this world

O ver and over again volcanoes erupting, it is like monsters

U nder the earth red-hot lava churning everywhere

N ever before seen this in my life

D inosaurs everywhere like a monstrous menace

L ucky for me I found a dark, gloomy shelter

O n the move again trying to get away from this place

S uddenly I see a dinosaur charging at me full charge

T hen I woke up and got away finally.

Charlie John Davis (10)

St Michael's Junior School, Galleywood

Fright Night

Z ombies around the corner
O MG the flesh is as green as emeralds
M um I wish I wasn't here in the frightening nightmare
B ang went the epic gunshot
I t had razor-sharp teeth
E yes were glancing at me with fear
S uddenly it was real

N ombie's haunted house had man-eating zombies
I t infected every human in the world
G o away zombies
H elp me now
T heir eyes glow like glow worms.

Jack Devey (9)
St Michael's Junior School, Galleywood

The Day The Bunnies Came

In this dreamland there is money, monsters, three
moons and some honey.
In the morning when I wake up I heard the shout of our
old folk.
He screamed because he had dropped some honey on
the poor three-legged bunny.
It hopped and squealed in pain as the man tried to
explain.
Then a load of bunnies came on a train to complain
about what he had done was a shame.
While this happened a boy bought a game which he
was going to claim.
This poem is going to explain about why you need to
pick my name.

Patrick Barrow (11)

St Michael's Junior School, Galleywood

Oh Dreams, Dreams, Dreams

Oh I have weird but amazing dreams...
That I can fly and read minds,
That my family was abducted by aliens
And that my friends all grew beards!

Oh I have weird but amazing dreams...
That pets looked after humans,
That dragons were really real,
And that pigs could fly!

Oh I have weird but amazing dreams...
That trees could walk,
That animals could talk,
And that everyone was friends.

Oh I have weird but amazing dreams...

Ethan Edwards (11)
St Michael's Junior School, Galleywood

Candy Land

As I close my eyes I once again enter Candy Land
Red skies at night, blue sky in the day.
Blue grass as far as the eyes can see
Waterfalls crashing everywhere.

Through the trees there it appears
The house of candy and gingerbread
The hot tub made of candyfloss
The Dairy Milk falls from the sky.

I love to visit this happy land
Each night I love to go there
But sadly dreams must come to an end
Slowly the morning sun arrives to wake me.

Rudy Don Golding (10)
St Michael's Junior School, Galleywood

Bogey Dreams

B ogeys, bogeys, everywhere
O ut of your nose they always appear
G reen, sticky things here and there
E asy to wipe and easy to smear
Y ou never know what bogeys are

D o I see a bogeyman
R ight here in this bogey land
E xcited I feel to meet these strange things
A re they good or are they bad
M aybe I'm stuck in Bogey Land
S uddenly I wake up in bed with a bogey on my
pillow.

Hollie Brook (9)
St Michael's Junior School, Galleywood

My Secret Powers

My midnight clock has struck at last
So now is the time it's been so fast
My pixies awaken
But my cat is shaken
Oreo now lays
And my pixies stay
My adventure awaits
At my pixies rate
Then I stop
Then I hop
My magic is working
And something is lurking
My leaf dress is on
And so's the hat I won
Now I'm in my magic room
And now I see a brush and broom
What fun will I have today
Let's look back to yesterday.

Issy Caviel (8)
St Michael's Junior School, Galleywood

A Dream For Tomorrow

O nce upon a dream
N o war, no hate
C lean water for everyone
E ducation for all.

U nity between countries
P oor countries helped
O ceans clean and full of fish
N o famines

A fun world of joy and laughter

D reams of love, joy and respect
R efugees have homes
E veryone loves each other
A free world
M agical friendship.

Tom Beales (10)
St Michael's Junior School, Galleywood

Fantasy Land

F luffy clouds made of candyfloss
A pple juice trickles from the clouds like rain
N o one is every angry here
T o live here you must remain
A kind soul at all times
S ugar sweet flowers bloom all around
Y ear after year the sun shines bright

L ove is all around here
A nd I lie here from morning to night
N obody else visits my world
D ue to it being only my fantasy dream.

Isla Gurden (11)
St Michael's Junior School, Galleywood

The Woods!

N othing is here in this strange place I see
I take a big step wondering where to go
G lancing left and right, thinking where am I
H ow did I get here?
T hud! I see yellow eyes peeping from all around
M y fear has been revealed - it's a killer clown
A huge grin smiles at me
R unning faster than a cheetah
E erie eyes are following me, I am close to dread
S oon I wake up, glad to be back.

Jonathan Wakeling (10)
St Michael's Junior School, Galleywood

I Had A Dream

I had a dream,
To be a famous astronaut getting lost in outer space.

I had a dream,
To one day see dragons, unicorns and wizards and witches.

I had a dream,
To be a fairy dancing as she flies.

I had a dream,
When monsters were athletes that had super powers.

I had a dream,
To be a wizard or witch teacher at Hogwarts.

I had a dream,
To one day see aliens crash into the London Eye.

Emma Cox (9)
St Michael's Junior School, Galleywood

Snakes Creating My Terror

N ightmare snakes swirling all around
I 'm the one lying on the ground
G iant cracks covering the Earth
H ere comes more snakes for what it's worth
T here must be a way to get away
M ore snakes keep appearing on this frightful day
A re there more snakes in the cracks?
R acing snakes leaving their tracks
E vening strikes, or is it morning?
S unshine wakes me, day is dawning.

Daniel Gardner (10)
St Michael's Junior School, Galleywood

My Trip

Wales so bright,
The grass so green,
The sheep so white
And the people as nice as we seem.

We went to a camp,
To have loads of fun
We slipped in the water and our feet got cramp
When it was better we went for a run.

There were mysteries to be found
About Wales health
Green and lovely the ground
This is good for your wealth.

I enjoyed my trip to Wales
I hope I come here again.

Sophie Shead (9)
St Michael's Junior School, Galleywood

The Creature Of The Deep

Myself and Alex were on the sea
We saw a golden key
In a big huge ship.

There's a shadow of an unknown creature
As tall as a tree.

My hand flings out and from it comes a gush of light
And the darkness disappears.

I hear a scream made out of fear
And then the monster flees.

Suddenly Alex flies towards the monster,
Who stops and turns...

Suddenly I'm awake.

Alasdair John Gray (9)
St Michael's Junior School, Galleywood

Untitled

All of the teachers in Mainland School were having
their break in the staff room
One of the teachers told a funny joke
Everyone laughed
Then the head teacher said we were under-staffed
Then ten unicorns said, 'Well be your staff
As long as you give us a bath.'

D ream
R emember
E nchanted
A lleyways
M arvellous

B ig Ben
I gloo
G iant.

Rhianna Riley (9)
St Michael's Junior School, Galleywood

Once Upon A Dream

Once upon a dream I dreamed about a dragon
Coming to destroy the whole world
Then a princess got a sword and swooped the dragon's
head off.

Once upon a dream I dreamed I found a snake
In the garden and kept it as a pet.

Once upon a dream I dreamed that a karate princess
came
And saved me from a giant.

Once upon a dream I dreamed that I met a wicked
wizard
He tried to turn me into a frog.

Chloe Southgate (8)
St Michael's Junior School, Galleywood

Jerry The Bear

Jerry the bear has lots of hair
I glanced in the air as I ate a pear
Jerry's not old and he's very cold
Jerry the bear didn't care
He wanted to eat a chocolate eclair
Jerry the bear didn't swear
He even ate a big eclair
Where, oh where, is Jerry the bear
He's sitting on the stairs
Jerry the bear ate a pear on the stair
He's very rare, oh Jerry the bear
Please eat a pear, Jerry the bear.

Jessica Barrow (9)
St Michael's Junior School, Galleywood

The Geese!

T he terrifying geese waddling towards me
H issing viciously just like an angry snake
E scape! Is there a way?

G lowing eyes like amber staring into your shivering soul
E erie shrill of their nightmarish calls
E xtremely puffed up feathers, ready to threaten
S pine-chilling shrieks from these petrifying birds
E ventually, I'm relieved, it's only a dream - but was is?

Millie Melvin (11)
St Michael's Junior School, Galleywood

Nightmare House

N ightmare crawl in this house
I n this house there is fear
G hastly, disgusting squeaky mouse
H aunted deadly ghosts I see a tear
T errifying scary killer clowns
M ighty spiders as hairy as a gorilla
A house that takes your pounds
R eached garden with crazy killer
E yes staring, bloodshot, glowing in the dull night
S uddenly the house was clear, it was Halloween.

Rebecca Samuels (10)
St Michael's Junior School, Galleywood

Once Upon My Nightmare

All of a sudden I was in a nightmarish world
Gloomy streets surrounding me
Clowns roaming around.

Skinny spider running up my shaking legs
Little children screaming for help
Mothers worried stiff.

Wolves howling towards the full moon,
Vampire wanting blood,
Ghosts haunting me.

All of this was roaming round my evil imagination,
It woke me up,
I screamed...

Chloe Bull (11)
St Michael's Junior School, Galleywood

Dreamland

It's upside down in Dreamland
And the sky is as green as an emerald
All on the floor is just clouds
People so cheerful all around
I went to a race and came first place
I won a big prize
I got a chip
I went back again
I fell off so I came in third place
I went back home and had a small pie
No one was happy in Dreamland
How sad it was to see that,
No one was happy in Dreamland.

Mia Coetser (8)
St Michael's Junior School, Galleywood

Fairies

F lying through the sky, that's where I want to be:

A dventures far and wide, there is so much we can see

I nvestigating places and finding our way around

R eaching for the stars, nothing is out of bounds

I nfinity and beyond, there is no holding back

E scaping into Dreamland, keeping me on track

S prinkle everyone with fairy dust, there is plenty in my sack.

Katie Walpole-Bennett (10)
St Michael's Junior School, Galleywood

Gunshots

G unshots flew horizontally at our faces

U nhappy and scared, something covered me, sacks of blood

N ever again something was holding me by the back

S outh we go and out we went

H e lifted me sadly over his back

O i! Oi! Shouts I heard

T ook a bullet to the head, I fell

S oldiers ran and routed their feet on the squelchy mud, Down I went with a thud!

Lauri Roberts (9)

St Michael's Junior School, Galleywood

Nightmare

N ot a piece of hair like a fish
 I couldn't wake up a
G rief pitch-black dream
H ow I was scared
T oo horrible to even open my eyes it is
M agical that finally I was starting to wake up blindly
A blink of a collapsed eye, I woke up
R unning as fast as I could to see if my mother was there
E nd of my bedroom - my mother was there.

Esme Alty (9)
St Michael's Junior School, Galleywood

The Best Dream

The sky was like emerald
It sparkled so bright
It brought the popcorn trees alight
The tall sunflowers took me so high
All the way up to the sky
Near the popcorn trees I could see a river
The reflection shimmered and made me shiver
A big yellow horse came so near
It lived for a thousand years
The thunder came down with a big frown
But it had a golden crown

Chloe Williams (10)
St Michael's Junior School, Galleywood

Football

When I'm an adult
I'm going to be
A football player.
The more I start
The more I score.
The more I play
The more fans cheer for me.
The more I play on the wing
The more skills I can do.
The more the manager
Stays up the more he is tired.
That night when
The moon was bright
It was way past
The manager's bedtime.

Harrison Whiteside (7)
St Michael's Junior School, Galleywood

The Magic Dream

Unicorns!
Unicorns are fluffy
Unicorns are cute
Unicorns are the best pet for you.

If you like magic get a unicorn,
If you have a wish, you should be a unicorn
If you had a unicorn it should be called Ruby.

While unicorns are not in danger
You should get one now
Go to Unicorn Land
It's the best place to be.

Evelyn Tumbridge (8)
St Michael's Junior School, Galleywood

The Unicorn

I dream of a magical unicorn
With a flowing mane and tail
Riding over a rainbow bursting with colour
Shiny sparkles and glittering lights that are in the sky
shining
As me, Jessica, Millie and Emily stroll across the path
We wander into a land of friendship
We feel excited and happy
As we ride amazing unicorns over the orange sunset.

Niamh Keenan (9)
St Michael's Junior School, Galleywood

Darkness Of Nightmares

I close my eyes and I can see
A big surprise scaring me.

The black dust, black sand
Wake up I must, this is not grand.

The big petrifying creatures scares my brightness
Nightmares have features, fires my lightness.

An evil jungle corrupt, the man of the shed
Then I wake up and I'm safe in bed.

Keziah Joy Burchell (9)
St Michael's Junior School, Galleywood

Canada

Canada is where I can see my favourite singers
Canada is where you don't have to go to school
Canada is a place for you
Canada is as calm as a restaurant
Canada is my dream
You would never went to leave
It's really fun
Canada has hotels made out of chocolate
You will have a better life
Canada has your dreams.

Weronika Piotrowska (8)
St Michael's Junior School, Galleywood

Dream Cats

D iving cats deep in the sea
R oller-skating cats with bright pink roller boots
E verlasting cats with infinite lives
A pple-eating cats which eat apples
M agnetic cats which attract metal

C ats are...
A thletic
T reasured
S uper and unique.

Imogen Ayres (8)
St Michael's Junior School, Galleywood

The Mines!

T o the mines I went to sleep
H e came to me, the dark shadow
E verything started to fade away

M e and my friends saw a way out
I hate bleak, dark mines, I
N ever can reach the end
E very dream was bad
S adly the dark shadow reached me.

Shay Turner (9)
St Michael's Junior School, Galleywood

Shaky Story

I'll tell you
But it might give you a fright
Don't read it at midnight
When the clock strikes twelve
It will give you a fright
Don't open your eyes
Or turn on the light
You're being watched by evil eyes
The silence will make you shake
But all will be safe when you wake.

Andrew Frain (10)
St Michael's Junior School, Galleywood

The Football Dream

The crowd were calling out their names
Jaiden, Olly, Harry, Bailey and James
The whistle blew,
The ball flew.
With a twist and a turn the amazing goal was scored
The whole stadium applauded
This was the Champions League Football Final match,
Olly turned and fell out of bed with a smash and bash.

Olly Sweeting (8)
St Michael's Junior School, Galleywood

Spiders

S piders in the shadows when I am in bed
P laying games
I deas they are thinking of indeed
D readful ones as horrible as a nightmare
E yes watching me like a lion, I feel terrified
R agged teeth or not, it's time to...
S creech! I am in its belly.

Oren Lindo (9)
St Michael's Junior School, Galleywood

Jony And The Dream

This is a boy called Jony
He went to bed and was in a house with sweets
The door is made out of fudge
Jony went inside with a massive cake
So he went towards it and made up a song just like this
I ate and ate until I was sick on the floor
I made and made to be especially four.

Lucian Richardson (7)
St Michael's Junior School, Galleywood

Revenge Of Darkness

Peace and happiness, laughter and joy all together
Having fun but soon... fades away, darkness returns,
Killing every life of nature, destroying everything until
The souls cry and the creatures bow down also making
the winds howl...
Until we go to unescapable... death.

Ruhayla Abdullah (8)
St Michael's Junior School, Galleywood

Night Fright

I woke up with a fright
I wouldn't sleep all night
My book fell off the shelf
Maybe it was a house elf
I tried to go to sleep
But there was too much sleet
I was thinking all day about sheep
I tried to creep
But all the cars beeped.

Alex Foulston (8)
St Michael's Junior School, Galleywood

Dreaming

D reading the monster
R unning for my life
E scaping from the
A fter getting a fright
M ore monsters are coming
 I am still going
N ever escaping
G ingerbread swords saving the day.

Konrad Philpott (10)
St Michael's Junior School, Galleywood

Summer's Day

Red rocks are as red as the sun
The wind snores loudly
Kites whooshing over the bright emerald grass
Dandelions jumping in the air
Oak trees waving their hands
Grass blowing kisses to the sky
Cute dogs waddling in the grass.

Max Baulch (8)
St Michael's Junior School, Galleywood

Dream Land

In a mystical land
There were pink and shiny unicorns
Unicorns are the best
They can fly up to the sky
Unicorns will let you ride them
If you be nice to them
They'll take you wherever you want.

Jasmine Ellouise Potter (8)
St Michael's Junior School, Galleywood

Dreams

D elight on your face
R ockets to racing cars
E xcitement everywhere
A nimals all around you
M onsters around every corner
S illy jokes from funny clowns.

Oliver Lakin (9)
St Michael's Junior School, Galleywood

Gingerbread House

Once upon my dream
I had to live in a gingerbread house
Bang!
As I jumped on the marshmallow trampoline
But it was upside down
I went down the window slide.

Katie Cox (7)
St Michael's Junior School, Galleywood

My Unicorn Dream

Deep in the jungle me and Lauren stared
A unicorn comes and it is as beautiful as my teacher
We walk towards it and I stroke it with my hand
We think it's an amazing creature.

The unicorn walks towards some trees,
We start to follow it into the darkness.
The unicorn goes on its back legs and eats some cheese
Then we suddenly scream with cuteness.

We look up to the sky
Then we carry on walking towards the unicorn
We look behind us and a unicorn shouts, Hi
It bends down and I see its spiky corn.

I start to look in front of me and I see a waterfall
In front of it is a big rock with two dancing jelly beans
The unicorn starts to speak and it says it's name is Paul
It starts to put on bright jolly jelly beans.

Mayeisha Pelis (9)
St Peter's Primary School, South Croydon

The Mean Clouds

Oh where are you
Oh where are you the puppy of my dreams?
I'm being chased by a horrifying cloud as fierce as a
lion
And I've been running mile after mile.

My legs are like steel and I can't use them at all
But my mouth is fine and not aching at all
I'm feeling too worn out, I don't dare to breathe
All I can do is cough and sneeze.

I then look ahead, but what do I see
Some more angry clouds staring at me
I'm very tired and my eyes start to close
I don't know how I'm going to manage without a little
doze.

I blink my eyes to try and stay awake
But then what do I see,
The puppy of my dreams!

Lola Manvatkar (8)
St Peter's Primary School, South Croydon

Wizards Battle

W here is it no one knows
I see a glistening red fire beam
Z ebras fighting in the background
A very strong wizard is showing off
R arely does a wizard ever fight a dragon
D umb wizards running about like crazy

B eneath a dragon is a rumbling sword
'A ttack,' said a dumb wizard
T ough dragons as strong as a rock
T earing limbs from limbs
L ime grass fresh and new
E very wizard is dead.

Reece Bailey (8)
St Peter's Primary School, South Croydon

The Australian Olympics

The bar awaits for me
I feel like the bar has eyes and is staring at me
I then hear them call 'Number 72 to the bar!'
I feel woozy as if I was on Mars.

All of the butterflies are swirling in my belly,
The crowds looks like jelly
I get onto the bar
I just want this to be done.

I go onto my next move,
I twist and turn and shiver in fear.
Seeing my hands on the bar I finish
But something strange...
The judge looks like a jam jar!

Lily Steele (8)
St Peter's Primary School, South Croydon

With My Mind On The Clouds

I'm in this place where all is loud,
It may be that I'm on a cloud
Not really, as the clouds are not loud,
But where am I?
Or my mind's on the clouds

And here, on the clouds
I dreamt about
What can I be
With my mind on a cloud?

A dentist I wish,
As my mum is one,
But will I become
If my mind's on the clouds?

Raluca Maria Tataru (9)
St Peter's Primary School, South Croydon

Me And My Pug, Stefan

Me and my pug Stefan
Found a fresh green field in the middle of Candyland
We see the sunset as we lie
We look up at the sky as it turns to midnight
Black sky with stars that glitter in such a beautiful way
In a weird way
The moon smiles at us
We see a statue of me and my pug, Stefan
Made out of solid chocolate.

Victoria Pliszka (8)
St Peter's Primary School, South Croydon

In Space

The blazing sun reflected off the moon
Shimmering stars glimmered and glistened
Making stunning shapes in the exciting darkness
One step further, two steps further, a low exotic growl
Coming from behind a rock an alarming noise
An alien! Back to the spaceship shut the door
Seat belt on.

Alice Peterson (8)
St Peter's Primary School, South Croydon

Dragon

In the sparkling cabin there was a boy with a dragon
He once set off on an adventure
But many times they got hungry
But one particular time they saw a village
Thinking of food they set off towards it
Crash! Jacob and his dragon fell into a pit
But soon they climbed out to joy.

Jacob Fitzgerald (9)
St Peter's Primary School, South Croydon

Wizards

W izards are magical
I love being a wizard it's true
Z ebras getting ready for battles
A m I loving it? Yes I am
R oast for dinner, delicious for me
D umb wizards aren't using their brains
S pells are causing.

Sarmad Ahmad (8)
St Peter's Primary School, South Croydon

Dazzling Star

S tupendous star as pure as honey
T ruly brilliant worth countless money
A mazing star you fill me with light
R adiant star come back tomorrow night.

Isaac Kirkwood-Ayres (8)

St Peter's Primary School, South Croydon

A Dream As A Rugby Player

My dream to be a rugby player was the best I've ever had.
Just being in that dream made me so glad.
Running down the pitch with the wind through my hair
It felt so real, like I really was there.

Ducking and dodging to the opposition's surprise,
I thought that I might just get the winning try!
But alas today just wasn't for me
As I was swatted away like an annoying bee.

But I passed to a teammate who avoided the tackle
Leaving them mouthing like a beached mackerel
We congratulated our teammate for the try
As we ran back to the centre with spirits sky high!

We had done our best we could do no more
Our coach was ecstatic with the score.
But I then woke up and it was all a dream
But I was ready to tell my team.

I knew the match was still to come
But I was ready and pumped for this one.
Later that day we walked onto the pitch
I looked across at my best friend Mitch.

He smiled at me and then I knew
Today was a day when dreams would come true.

Freddie Lawler (10)
Vinehall School, Mountfield

My Fantastic Dream

I found Newt's case
And peeped inside
I climbed onto the ladder
And started to slide.

I reached the bottom
And looked around
And that was when
I heard the sound.

I saw a trail
A trail of gold
In front of my eyes
Was a sight to behold.

A Niffler
With his pouch full of jewels
He still needs to learn
To follow the rules.

Up in the sky
A Thunderbird flies
Conjuring storms
That make people cry.

Onto my shoulder
A Bowtruckle jumps
He whispers so softly
It gives me goosebumps.

I pick up a cocoon
And throw it around
Out comes Swooping Evil
With blue and green as its crown.

All around me are fantastic beasts
Fwoopers, Moon Calves and Murtlap
To name but a few
I must be dreaming,
It cannot be true.

Annabel Aoife Quill (10)
Vinehall School, Mountfield

Dreamare

D are I go downstairs tonight, or I might get a scary fright...

R ight underneath me I heard a bang, I heard a crash, I heard a clang

E eek, my bed went when I stepped down, I felt like I was having a nervous breakdown!

A round me was silent and all I could see was the very bright moon as full as could be...

M y fingers were tingling as I walked the last stair, I wonder what's in that room, I was still unaware;

A t last I would find what's in that room, it might be a ghost or a witch with a broom

R eaching to the light switch I noticed something funny, it had a long tail and looked like a bunny...

E xamining it closer it was holding a string ball, oh no, it's my cat after all!

Dexter Bell (10)
Vinehall School, Mountfield

Acting

The movie is showing the people aren't going
Until the movie's ended
But no, the audience are annoyed,
The sounding's destroyed.
The movie's a fail
The cinema manager wants to bail.
But luckily this won't happen to me.
When I'm older,
And strong enough to catch a boulder,
I'll be an actor, and a good one too.
I'll show the world, what I can do,
And have fun until the end.
And I'll be in a new movie without a doubt.
And this time at the cinema, hopefully,
The manager won't be kicked out.
This is my dream and I hope it will come true.
But right now, I'm writing this poem
For you!

Billy Mannion (10)
Vinehall School, Mountfield

Black Cat

Soft and silent on velvet paws
He creeps inside my bedroom door...
The black cat!
His eyes gleam orange in the darkness
His tail swishes through the midnight blackness
Why is he here?
What does he want?
He searches the room in an elegant hunt
Behind open cupboards
Brushing the curtains
He settles on the window sill
I see his silhouette against the moonlit sky
In a puff of smoke he vanishes
I wake to see my ginger cat
Asleep on my warm soft lap.

Tilly Richardson (9)
Vinehall School, Mountfield

Deep In The Night

Deep in the night
When you're all asleep
A small little monster
Alone he creeps.
He draws himself
Into your mind
And these are the fantastic
Things he finds.
He walks into a candy land
He meets a small gingerbread man
As tiny as a jelly bean.
He meets a monster same size as he
She walks towards him with a smile
And together they walk for miles...
So that monster mean and small
Did find love after all.

Connie Soan (10)
Vinehall School, Mountfield

In A Magical Dream

In a magical world,
Everything's as happy as a rainbow,
Houses, a third sea, a third Earth and a third sky
And a roof a rainbow.

The sun shines happily
The snow jumps for joy every day
The giants have wings as big as trees
They also have force fields around their bodies,
They can go underwater.

The birds tweet in harmony
The bees bark
And candy grows
It was unfortunately just a dream.

Gabriella America Brewer (10)
Vinehall School, Mountfield

The Shape-Shifter

It moves around, high and low
knocking trees down, down and below.
Up in the sky, it whirls and it twirls
around and around
will it ever reach the ground?
Who could it be?
What could it be; will we ever find out
Maybe!
It was a leaf as light as a feather,
carried by the stormy, windy weather,
And hey we worked it out -
what a wonderful way
to end the day!

Edith Daphne Forder (9)
Vinehall School, Mountfield

Monsters Under Your Bed

Oh have you ever seen them under your bed
With their claws and their fingers and their toothy grin?

Oh have you heard the devilish laugh
Have you heard all of them?
Then you have monsters staying!

Isak Syltevik Dobson (10)
Vinehall School, Mountfield

Est.1991

YOUNG WRITERS
INFORMATION

We hope you have enjoyed reading this book – and
that you will continue to in the coming years.

If you're a young writer who enjoys reading and creative writing,
or the parent of an enthusiastic poet or story writer,
do visit our website **www.youngwriters.co.uk**. Here you will
find free competitions, workshops and games, as well as
recommended reads, a poetry glossary and our blog.

If you would like to order further copies of this book,
or any of our other titles, then please give us a
call or visit **www.youngwriters.co.uk**.

Young Writers
Remus House
Coltsfoot Drive
Peterborough
PE2 9BF
(01733) 890066
info@youngwriters.co.uk